Introduction

Since ancient times linen cloth has been made in Ireland from flax grown on farms and small holdings, but the roots of Irish linen manufacture – which was world renowned by the end of the nineteenth century – did not start to form until the 1700s.

During the seventeenth century the cultivation of flax for cloth was encouraged by plantation landlords to supplement farming incomes. It received further impetus when new weaving techniques and equipment were brought in by French Huguenots who settled in the Lisburn area in 1698.

The output from the spinning and weaving of linen increased throughout the eighteenth century and developed as a business thanks to the entrepreneurship of the linen bleachers who bought up the newly woven brown linen in the markets throughout the country. It was also supported by financial assistance for equipment from the Irish Linen Board, founded in 1715. A linen hall was built in Dublin as a trading centre but when bleachers from Ulster began to export their cloth from Belfast the main activity for linen became concentrated in the North. After that more linen mills were established in Ulster and bleach greens were set up with watermills on the principal river valleys such as the Upper Bann, the Lagan, the Callan, Main and Sixmilewater.

By the early nineteenth century textile production was also centred on spinning cotton thread using raw cotton imported from England. It was a sizeable industry, particularly around Belfast, employing hundreds in mills that were built close to sea ports. When cotton became less profitable producers sought commercial methods of spinning linen yarn instead. The invention of the wet spinning process in the 1820s, enabling brittle flax fibres to be spun mechanically without breaking, provided the necessary technique. This was exploited first at Mulholland's spinning mill in Belfast, which was burnt down in 1828. The premises were restored with wet spinning machinery, reopening in 1930. The mill was to become known as the York Street Spinning Mills. After that success more mills were established in Ulster, mainly concentrated in Belfast, but also in villages and towns throughout the province.

From the mid-nineteenth century weaving became heavily industrialised although hand weaving continued on a domestic scale for the production of very fine damask cloth. The linen industry prospered and enjoyed a boom in the 1860s during the American Civil War when cotton imports from America were blockaded, creating a greater demand for linen. Output was so large that flax had to be imported from abroad, mainly Russia, as not enough could be grown at home. Ulster's wet and unpredictable weather conditions could also create an uncertain crop yield.

In the early 1900s the Ulster linen industry peaked as the largest in the world. According to an official estimate in 1910, the export of linen piece goods from Belfast was more than the export of all continental countries combined. Linen products ranged from threads and nets to damask napkins and tablecloths to handkerchiefs, sheets, towels, clothing, canvas, buckrams, tenting and interlinings. Demand for heavy cloth was high during the First World War due to the need for materials for uniforms, tents, stretchers, kitbags, vehicle seat interlinings and aeroplane wings.

During the inter-war years demand for linen declined as fashions and lifestyles started to modernise. Women's clothing, for example, was simplified with shorter skirts and fewer layers of undergarments. There was less interest in clothes and fabrics that would last a lifetime, one of linen's selling points, and better off households had fewer servants to launder cumbersome household linen.

Although the outbreak of the Second World War boosted demand for military equipment again and the growing of flax was encouraged by government subsidies, the linen industry continued to shrink. Competition from cheap Far Eastern cotton imports and manmade fibres, and increasing demand for lighter, more easily maintained clothing and furnishing fabrics, hastened the decline from the 1950s onwards. Factories and mills closed down and were largely gone by the 1970s, leaving today barely a handful of old linen firms such as Ferguson's of Banbridge and William Clark and Sons in Upperlands which have created successful specialisms within the textile industry.

Taken from a field above the Lurgan Road outside Dromore, this photograph shows Murphy and Stevenson's Holm weaving factory and the viaduct beyond. The view has changed relatively little since, except for the disappearance of the factory chimney. The terrace of red brick workers' cottages was designed by the architect Henry Hobart who lived at Lagan Lodge; after his apprenticeship with William Henry Lynn, he set up a practice which continues today as Hobart Heron architects. Dromore on the River Lagan was the site of bleach greens in the eighteenth century and various factories for hemstitching and cambric production grew up there in the nineteenth century. The Holm factory was later taken over by Ewart Liddell of Donaghcloney and was used for machine stitching and as a warehouse. The buildings are now used by the Mulgrew road haulage company.

The Irish Linen Industry

by Rose Jane Leslie

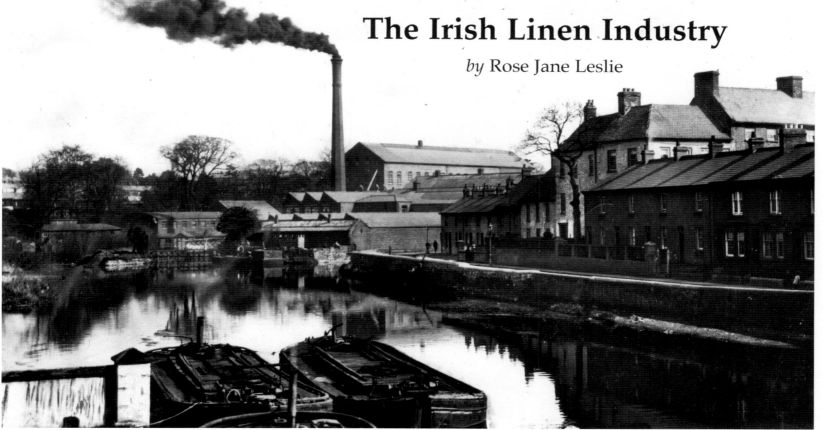

A view from the Union Bridge in Lisburn, looking over the River Lagan towards the Island Spinning Mill which covered some three acres between the canal and the river. A flax spinning mill was built there in 1840 and the Island Spinning Co. established in 1867, while a large weaving factory was added a few years later. In 1882 the factory had also started to produce threads for hand and machine sewing that were exported to Europe and America, employing over 1,100 workers. The mill belonged to the Clarke family until Mr Edward Stanley Clarke retired in 1952; it closed about 1960. The site was redeveloped as the Island Arts Centre and council buildings, which opened in 2001. In the eighteenth century the site was known as Vitriol Island after the vitriol that was made there from sulphuric acid and other chemicals and used as a bleaching agent for linen which was treated on the many greens near Lisburn and the Upper Bann Valley. Coal for the factory was transported from Belfast along the Lagan Canal in barges, or 'lighters', seen here in the foreground.

Text © Rose Jane Leslie, 2018.
Photographs from the Des Quail Collection.
First published in the United Kingdom, 2018,
by Stenlake Publishing Ltd.
Telephone: 01290 551122
www.stenlake.co.uk

Printed by Berforts, 17 Burgess Road, Hastings, TN35 4NR

ISBN 9781840338287

**The publishers regret that they cannot supply
copies of any pictures featured in this book.**

Acknowledgements

The author would like to thank Bruce Clark for lending additional photographs from William Clark and Sons, and the Irish Linen Centre, Lisburn Museum, for assistance with research.

Further Reading

The books listed below were used by the author during her research. None of them are available from Stenlake Publishing. Those interested in finding out more are advised to contact their local bookshop or reference library.

Jonathan Bardon, *A History of Ulster*, Blackstaff Press 1992.
Wallace Clark, *Linen on the Green*, Universities Press 1982.
W. A. McCutcheon, *The Industrial Archaeology of Northern Ireland*, 1980.
Marilyn Cohen, *Linen Family and Community in Tullylish, County Down 1690–1914*, Four Courts Press 1997.
Peter Collins, *The Making of Irish Linen*, Friars Bush Press 1994.
Betty Messenger, *Picking up the Linen Threads*, Blackstaff Press 1998.
Kathleen Rankin, *Linen Houses of the Bann Valley*, Ulster Historical Foundation 2007.
Kathleen Rankin, *Linen Houses of the Lagan Valley*, Ulster Historical Foundation 2002.
Kathleen Rankin, *Linen Houses of County Antrim and North Down*, Ulster Historical Foundation 2012.
County Armagh 100 Years Ago: a Guide and Directory 1886, G.H. Bassett 1988.
County Down 100 Years Ago: a Guide and Directory 1888, G.H. Bassett 1989.
From Flax to Fabric, Irish Linen Centre and Lisburn Museum 1994.

William Liddell was the founder of this damask weaving factory in Donaghcloney, set up in the 1860s beside the River Lagan on the site of an eighteenth-century bleach works. The long building dates from 1816 and is the oldest industrial building at the site. It was first used to boil and prepare yarn for handloom weavers. The three-storey building beside the chimney housed the design department and a doctor's surgery. Just beyond it, the structure with the roof cupola contained the steam engine. These buildings remain standing, though derelict, but the numerous weaving sheds and the mill pond have gone. The area of the allotments in the left foreground has been redeveloped with housing.

In the early twentieth century Liddell's was one of the principal damask weaving factories in the province and employed about 1,000 workers. Donaghcloney village grew up to house the factory workers and families for whom a school was also provided. The factory management also made a cricket ground with surrounding cycling track, tennis courts and allotments for the workers. However, compared to the present day, rules for workers were strict. The terms and conditions of employment in 1911 stated that any worker absent without prior arrangement could be fined 2*d* and any worker absent after a meal hour would have to pay 3*d*. Each employee was expected to clean any machine under their charge every Saturday and any breach of this would incur a fine of 6*d*. Deductions from wages could also be taken for incompetent work. Liddell died in 1901 but the company continued in business for many years and in 1973 it merged with William Ewart & Sons of Belfast. Ewart Liddell was acquired by Baird McNutt in 2001.

DONACLONEY FACTORY LOOKING SOUTH

All Saints Parish Church of Ireland is in the foreground of this photograph of Tullylish village taken in the 1920s. In the background is Banford bleach green, one of the largest of the greens established along the banks of the Upper Bann river between Banbridge and Gilford from the eighteenth century. The terrain, with wide flat fields extending to the river's edge, lent itself to spreading yards of newly woven linen fabric to be bleached white from its natural pale brown colour. On this stretch of the river the water was clear and suitable for bleaching. Further upstream, near Gilford, bleaching did not take place as the river water was stained brown due to seapage from adjacent peat bogs at Moyallen. Many of the bleaching businesses on the Upper Bann were set up by interrelated Quaker families such as the Christys, Richardsons, Wakefields, Uprichards, Nicholsons and Phelps who migrated to this part of Ireland during the eighteenth century.

A closer view of the Banford Bleach Works buildings in the early twentieth century. As indicated by the various styles and designs of these structures, the works had developed in stages since the eighteenth century. The most recent additions were the Belfast trussed roofs added to the buildings on the right, a roofing method in which felted asphalt was stretched over a rounded wooden trellis. These roofs could be made elsewhere and erected on site and were an economic means of roofing a long low building suitable for bleaching processes. From the late-nineteenth century trussed roofing was used to replace older structures which had become unsafe due to corrosion caused by bleaching chemicals. Most of these buildings are still recognisable on the site which now contains a restaurant and ceramics studio. Notice the watch hut at the centre, near the piles of cloths banked up outside the two-storey building. Such huts were necessary for guarding from theft the valuable linen webs which were left outside for up to two weeks. In the eighteenth century, before chemical methods developed, this period would be even longer.

BANFORD BLEACH
GREEN.

BANFORD HOUSE. BLEACH GREEN.

In the early 1900s Banford House belonged to Frederick Sinton who had bought the property in the late-nineteenth century. He was the fifth son of Thomas Sinton of Laurelvale, near Tandragee where there was another notable linen factory. The house, which is about a mile outside Gilford, was built about 1780 by Thomas Nicholson whose father set up the bleachworks there, but he sold the works and the house to Benjamin Haughton in 1815. Frederick Sinton died in 1943, though his widow lived on there until 1968 when the house was sold. The front of the house has hardly changed though Frederick Sinton built a wing at the back to help accommodate his eight children.

Hazelbank at Coose townland, also in Tullylish Parish, was set up by Samuel Law in the 1830s and is thought to have been the oldest linen factory on the Upper Bann. The Hazelbank Weaving Company, shown here, was founded in 1880 by Thomas Dickson and William Walker. By 1889 there were 200 power looms and additional buildings including a weaving shed and two preparing sheds covering a site of seventeen acres. Forty-three workmens' cottages were also built by the firm, although many of the workers were girls from farming families who lived close enough to walk to work at the factory. Cloth produced at Hazelbank included drills, rough brown, buckrams and glass cloth from linen yarn transported by rail from Belfast. The factory closed in 1963.

Bleach Works; Lenaderg.

The largest bleach works along the Upper Bann was Milltown at Lenaderg. The founder, William Smyth, purchased the land in 1820 and by the 1860s the works had the capacity to produce 120,000 pieces of 30-yard cloth lengths per year, and had offices in London, Manchester and America. In 1888 the works had over 250 employees. The firm continued until 1941 when a fire in the bleaching and finishing works led to a decision to liquidate the company voluntarily. A financial provision made through a scheme of the Ulster Bleachers Association enabled Milltown Bleachworks to operate until the 1950s when the factory was closed; the buildings were demolished soon after.

BLEACH GREEN LENADERG.

In its heyday the Miltown Bleach Works, a concern that also operated as manufacturer, finisher and merchant, extended over some 220 acres. The works included a foundry with workshops equipped to cast and fit machinery parts needed on the site, which was powered by steam and water driven by six waterwheels. There was a railway siding, seen at the centre of the image, linked to the Great Northern Line to transport finished goods to Belfast.

The Dam, Banbridge

Photo (1924) by COON, Letterkenny.

A few miles upstream from Lenaderg, the town of Banbridge had become by 1820 an important linen market and production centre. By 1900 it had six linen factories. This view of the dam looks across towards the factory on the Castlewellan Road with the spire of Seapatrick Church beyond it. The railway line opened in 1859 to connect Banbridge and Scarva and the link to Belfast opened in 1863.

The Thomas Ferguson Ltd. Factory, Banbridge. Photo (1924) by COON, Letterkenny.

Ferguson's linen factory was on the river bank at Edenderry, on the Lurgan Road side of Banbridge, adjacent to the Academy where the large house built by Thomas Ferguson is now used by the school. The site was acquired by Ferguson in 1855 and the factory had started power loom weaving by 1866. There was a yarn treatment works beside the river and weaving sheds up the hill, as seen beside the chimney. Initially, Ferguson's made hucks and towelling, then introduced damask weaving in the early twentieth century. Over time the company adapted to changing market conditions and by the 1950s also produced damask made from cotton and rayon. In the 1970s Ferguson's supplied towelling products to hotels and airlines while keeping a niche in double damask. The company was sold to Franklin and Sons in the 1980s and moved to new premises on the Scarva Road, but it is still called Ferguson's Irish Linen today.

Photographed in 1912, these men were employed as linen 'lappers' by Thomas Ferguson and Co. Their job was to fold, prepare and pack finished linen products for dispatch to destinations all over the world. By this time the meaning of the term lapper had changed somewhat since it was first used in the eighteenth century, when it applied to those appointed to inspect and stamp white linen for its quality. From left these men are Richard Downey, Walter Thomson, Charlie McCourt, George Kelly, Bob Aulds, Alfred Martin, Jimmy McKinley, Ernie Thompson, Jim Smyth, Walter Gosling, John Savage and John McAdam.

The lapping room of William Clark and Sons at Upperlands, Co. Londonderry, newly built in 1930 after a fire in October 1929, which may have been started by an electric iron left switched on. It destroyed the old lapping room, stock room and company offices. At that time Clark's produced and finished fabrics that included linen canvas, household fabrics, jute paddings and haircloths sold to the UK and exported overseas, particularly to Scandinavia, the United States and South Africa. Founded in 1736 with a bleachworks and beetling mill, the business is one of the oldest linen firms in Ireland. It continues today and is distinguished as the only Ulster linen firm in which descendants of the founder are still actively involved.

A new head office building was constructed at William Clark and Sons after the previous building was destroyed in the fire of 1929. Despite the destruction a substantial quantity of cloth was saved after the fire and shipped two days later. Makeshift offices were created in the homes of Clark family members, Ardtara House and Ampertaine House, as a temporary measure until the rebuild was completed the following year.

Photo (1924) by Coon, Letterkenny.　　　Bellevey Mill, near Banbridge.

A view from the 1920s that emphasises the antiquity of the bleachworks and beetling mill at Ballievey which was founded in the mid eighteenth century on the south side of the River Bann, a few miles outside Banbridge. The supporting pillars in the foreground are the remains of an old wooden bridge mentioned in the Ordnance Survey memoirs of 1834. At that time the mill was provided with a new waterwheel and was capable of producing 12,000 to 13,000 pieces of linen a year. In later years turbines were installed and used in the early twentieth century to generate electricity for Ballievey House which stood above the mill. Between the wars a new Ballievey bleach works was built at Corbet, a short distance up the river. This finally closed in 2008 and the site is now occupied by film studios and two other businesses including Ulster Weavers.

Laurelvale village, situated about a mile and a half from Tandragee, was originated as a model village to provide accommodation for workers at Sinton's linen factory, founded there around 1850. The family also built Laurelvale House in the village. At its peak the mill had 1,000 workers engaged in the manufacture of very high grade heavy linen until 1945 when it was taken over by the Ministry of Defence to produce ball bearings for tank turrets, a concern operated by Hoffman's. This photograph, sent as a postcard in 1907, shows the factory buildings and a row of mill workers cottages on the left, Cochrane's Hill, now gone. The factory was also destroyed by fire also in the 1970s. Since then the industrial site and Laurelvale House have been demolished and redeveloped. Laurelvale village has changed entirely and any reminders of the linen industry remain only in the names of housing developments such as Old Mill Manor and in the memories of local people.

Cochrane's Hill & Factory Laurelvale

A picture of Sinton's mill and workers' houses at Tandragee, taken around 1905, the year when Thomas Sinton, linen manufacturer and flax spinners, became a limited company. The firm, founded at Laurelvale, acquired the Tandragee mill in the 1870s. The mill operated until the mid 1990s and in its latter years spun thread of combined flax and artificial fibre, supplying companies such as Spence Bryson, Blacker's Mill, Moygashel and Ulster Weavers. Until 2003 the premises belonged to the Sinton family. Proposals for schemes to develop the property for residential use have as yet not come to fruition. Today the main factory building, chimney and associated structures that lie just beyond Mill Row behind the stone bridge are recognisable though derelict. Mill Row was demolished in the 1970s and replaced with modern housing. There is also housing development to the left of the background, on the site of the outlying factory buildings.

Gilford Spinning Mill

The group of children are standing outside the entrance of Gilford Mill at the end of a day's work and were probably employed to remove the full spindles of thread and replace them with empty ones, supervised by the doffing mistresses who would be among the women also seen here coming out of the mill. Legislation introduced in 1901 stipulated that children no younger than twelve could be employed but until then a child could have started work aged eight to supplement the family income. They worked alternate days as 'half timers' – Monday, Wednesday and Friday one week, Tuesday and Thursday the next. In between they attended school. In Gilford three schools were provided by the mill. At its height Gilford Spinning Mill employed around 1,500 people. The thread produced was exported to the USA, Canada, Australia, South America, the British colonies and throughout the British Isles. Built in 1834–39 on the banks of the River Bann, it finally closed in 1986 and the mill building with its distinctive wrought iron entrance gates now stands empty.

FACTORY LAURELVALE

In the late-nineteenth century Laurelvale, a few miles outside Tandragee, was sometimes referred to as Sintonville after the Sinton family under whom linen manufacture began here in the 1850s. Linen was spun for canvas and buckram. Records show that in 1887 some 600 people were employed and there were 350 looms. The factory relied on steam power from coal transported via the Newry Canal. Linen yarn was also put out to 1,500 cottage weavers locally and in Co. Down from another Sinton mill at Killyleagh. Production continued at Laureldale until the 1990s but since then the industrial buildings have been demolished.

Glen Mill and Viaduct, Keady

In South Armagh a significant linen industry developed near Keady on the Clea river, a tributary of the River Callan. The old beetling mill with louvred windows has been demolished but the railway viaduct in the background still stands. It was built between 1904 and 1909 on the Armagh to Castleblayney railway line that was only in use for around twenty years as it closed in 1924.

A stylised panoramic illustration of 1912 showing the Annavale bleaching works near Keady. It shows the extent of the linen industry that developed in the rolling countryside of the River Callan valley, where as early as 1771 there were 36 bleach yards. Annavale was described in Basset's Directory in 1889 as one of the largest bleach greens in Ireland, covering about 250 acres of land which was used for spreading linen, works and factories where weaving, dyeing, bleaching and finishing. There was a concentration of other bleach works situated in the locality to reach a distance of six miles along the Callan valley. Overlooking the bleach greens is the house of the owner William Kirk, under whose entrepreneurship Annavale developed from about 1840. After he died in 1871 the enterprise continued as the two firms of William Kirk and Partners and William Kirk and Co. William Kirk and Partners had a Belfast warehouse on Donegall Square West and agencies in New York, London and Manchester. William Kirk and Co. operated the mills at Darkley close by (see opposite).

The location of Darkley, several miles from Keady, was particularly remote in the nineteenth century when people relied on transport by foot and by horseback. The village was built in stages to house workers at the mill which was established around 1830 by James McKean. In 1845 it was taken over by William Kirk, McKean's son in law, who already owned a beetling mill there. Kirk also acquired bleach yards a few miles away at Annavale and he expanded the enterprise at Darkley, installing a 70-foot waterwheel – thought to be the second largest mill wheel in Europe – to power the extensive pinning and power loom weaving activities. Kirk died in 1902 but the Darkley enterprise continued to function until 1959. Today the village is recognisable from the photograph by the factory chimney on the main street and several factory buildings above the old cricket field that was created for the benefit of mill workers in the time of William Kirk.

Upper Mills, Glen Anne, Co. Armagh.

In another remote rural area four miles from Markethill, John Compton and Sons' factory at Glenanne was a leading manufacturer of ticking for mattress covers from the 1930s until the 1970s. At first the fabric was linen but in later years was woven from artificial silk and cotton threads. After that the product faced increased pressure from manufacturers in Belgium where the flax industry was subsidised and the Glenanne factory was eventually taken over by a Belgian company in 1988 but closed in 2009. The building shown here, built from light Paleozoic limestone that is characteristic of buildings in Armagh, was demolished in 2014. This ended the history of the mill building which dated from 1816.

On the northern end of the Callan river valley the bleach works at Milford were founded by William McCrum in 1808. In this view the men are in the process of gathering up and moving long, damp, webs of linen to be washed indoors. Linen webs would have been left on the field twice for up to two weeks each time for the process of atmospheric bleaching, between washing, soaking and boiling. Long hours were demanded of the bleach green workers during the summer months to make the most of the daylight and they were also expected to work into the night to move the fabric and ensure that it did not dry out in the field. Workers in the bleaching department washed the linen and applied chemical treatments to the cloth to alter its natural brown state. Linen that was to be sold white was prepared by the bluer who tinted and dyed fabric or yarn with substances such as Victoria blue colouring matter or Ultramarine in a liquid suspension. The beetler operated the beetling machine which pounded the cloth with wooden mallets to give the fabric a glazed finish. The callendar man operated the machine which rolled the woven linen under high pressure to smooth and thin the material.

Inside the wash room at the McCrum's factory where linen towels, damask cloth and sheeting were cleaned after being laid out on the field. Lengths of linen were passed through machinery suspended from above that squeezed it back and forward. In the bleaching process cloth was also soaked in hydrochloric and sulphuric acid, washed, then boiled for eight to ten hours, washed and boiled again, returned to the field for up to ten days, then brought in again and washed once more. Finally, the pieces were sewn together, passed through a mangle and plaited into trucks seen here, and then taken for beetling in which the cloth was pummelled to a fine glazed patina by means of the callendar and beetling machines.

Moyallen House, Gilford, Co. Down.

Two miles from Gilford, Moyallon House was by the turn of the twentieth century occupied by the Richardson family of Bessbrook Mill. John Grubb Richardson, who became sole owner of the mill in 1863, had married Jane Wakefield who was left Moyallon by her father Thomas Christy Wakefield. The house dates from 1794, replacing an earlier one there which belonged to Thomas Christy whose forebears came from Scotland and first introduced linen bleaching to the locality in the seventeenth century. The Christy family, along with the Richardsons and Wakefields, were all Quakers who were interlinked through marriage and their shared involvement in the linen industry of the Upper Bann Valley. Moyallon is still owned by Richardson family members.

29

Bessbrook Mill with a glimpse of the village beyond, a view taken from a position near Deramore House to the west. The variety and bulk of the buildings indicates the scale of the operation where there was a weaving factory with over 500 looms producing various linen goods from fine cambric to heavy canvas and damask. Other activities here included yarn boiling, beetling and bleaching, although the main bleaching green for Bessbrook Mill was the Glenmore bleach green at the village of Lambeg, near Lisburn. The operation was run under the name of Messrs Richardson, Sons and Owden Ltd, who had a head office and warehouse on Donegall Square, Belfast, in the building now occupied by Marks and Spencer. John Grubb Richardson of Moyallon House became sole owner of the works in 1863 and instigated the construction of Bessbrook village, an early model of town planning intended to provide a pleasant living environment for employees with well-built terraced housing, large squares and public buildings. In accordance with Richardson's Quaker values of peace, simplicity and community, the village did not include a public house, pawn shop or police station.

Bessbrook Spinning Mills as seen from the Pond Field.

The mill pond at Bessbrook covers a large area of water diverted from the River Camlough. The river gave rise to the 'brook' in the name of the village while 'Bess' was named for Elizabeth Richardson, wife of John G. Richardson. To the left of where the chimney stood the little tree-covered island looks much the same, as does the large grey factory building which today is listed B1 though more and larger trees have grown up in front of it. Manufacturing ceased at Bessbrook in the early 1970s following a decline in demand for linen products against cotton and synthetic textiles. The mill was requisitioned for use as a base by the British Army in 1972 and remained in that use until 2007. It is now vacant and on the Buildings at Risk register.

In 1913 weavers and winders employed in factories in Lurgan went on strike for five weeks in January and February, involving some 6,000 people employed in the town which had been an important linen producer for over 200 years. The workers, whose wage had remained the same since the 1880s sought a wage increase to a farthing per yard for the linen cloth they wove. As the photograph indicates, the workforce of weavers in the Lurgan linen industry was predominantly male. Usually, elsewhere, women did weaving but circumstances here differed as weaving was the main employment available so females tended to be winders instead. During the strike the factories were closed and workers received some financial support from trade unions, though not all workers were members. During the strike women were employed with outwork from the hem stitching factories in the town. In the end the workers voted to accept a wage increase of half a farthing.

This postcard commemorated the construction in the late-nineteenth century of a new weaving factory at Lurgan, a business bought over from James Macoun under whom cambric had been made since the 1860s. The single-storey building, near the town centre, is a characteristic late-Victorian weaving shed with a saw-toothed roof which had glass skylights to illuminate the interior with north light which is bright and constant, ideally suited to producing and inspecting textiles. In summer a glass roof might be whitewashed to reduce the heat and glare. Inside it was necessary to maintain a steamy, warm environment to prevent the linen threads from drying and breaking and to this end there were no side windows to prevent warm dry air from blowing in. In the early twentieth century the humidity in weaving rooms was also raised sometimes by using nozzles eight foot high to blow steam around the shed. Weaving was regarded as more skilled than spinning and wages were somewhat higher though workers were paid according to the output of cloth they produced.

Previous page: The scene inside the weaving room at the Ewart factory on Crumlin Road, Belfast, before the looms have started working for the day. The factory had 1,000 looms operated by 500 employees. The warp threads, which run the full length of the fabric (the web), are waiting on large spools as wide as the fabric, while in the rack above the conical spools hold the thread which crosses the fabric (the weft). These are waiting to fill the shuttles, which are loaded into the long torpedo-like 'beds' seen beside the webs. When the machines start the shuttle passes back and forth across the fabric mesh to weave the fabric. These looms produced simple patterns or plain fabrics. Elsewhere in the factory there was more complex machinery to lift the warp thread according to a pattern to produce damask linen.

Right: Weaving by handloom continued until the early twentieth century alongside mechanisation as the output remained sought after for its softness and quality compared to machine-woven cloth. A weaver in Waringstown, where this highly skilled craft had been practiced since the seventeenth century, is at work on a jacquard loom. The jacquard system used cards punched with holes to produce self-coloured patterns in the cloth showing intricate designs of flowers, crests and coats of arms. Before weaving, the threads were prepared with a solution of flour and water to prevent them from drying up and breaking during the process. It could take a week to set up a jacquard handloom for weaving in a cottage. The linen produced was sold in prominent outlets such as Robinson and Cleaver's department store in Belfast, where the high status of the work was highlighted in their advertising: 'Handloom weaving is not easy work and calls for a strong man as well as skilful.'

A Damask Napkin Handloom Weaver, Warringstown.

Outside the linen mills and factories women were also engaged as outworkers to hand-embroider linen handkerchiefs, napkins and tablecloths. The work was known as sprigging or flowering and is shown here with the girl's work being held in place with an embroidery frame. She is wearing an embroidered linen collar which would have been fashionable at the time. The picture was taken in the Co. Down village of Hilltown. In this county, along with Co. Armagh and the Lagan, home workers would have received sewing from the factories, while in north-west Ulster linen parcels were sent from Belfast linen warehouses by rail.

On an upper floor of the Walpole Brothers' Linen Warehouse, a five-storey redbrick warehouse built on the corner of Albert Street, Belfast, in 1911–12, machine stitchers are at work on fine table linen. After the acquisition of John Hennings and Son's damask manufacturers at Waringstown in 1885, and a hemstitching factory in Lurgan, the firm branched into fine linen production with offices in Dublin, Belfast and London. At the end of the nineteenth century Ulster was the main producer of fine embroidered handkerchiefs, underclothing and shirts. By the 1930s demand for such linen products had declined and during the Second World War the firm produced aeroplane linen under contract from the government (in 1939 defence contracts worth £6 million were given to Northern Ireland by the British Government). Linen continued to be manufactured until the 1960s after which the factory was used to make boilers.

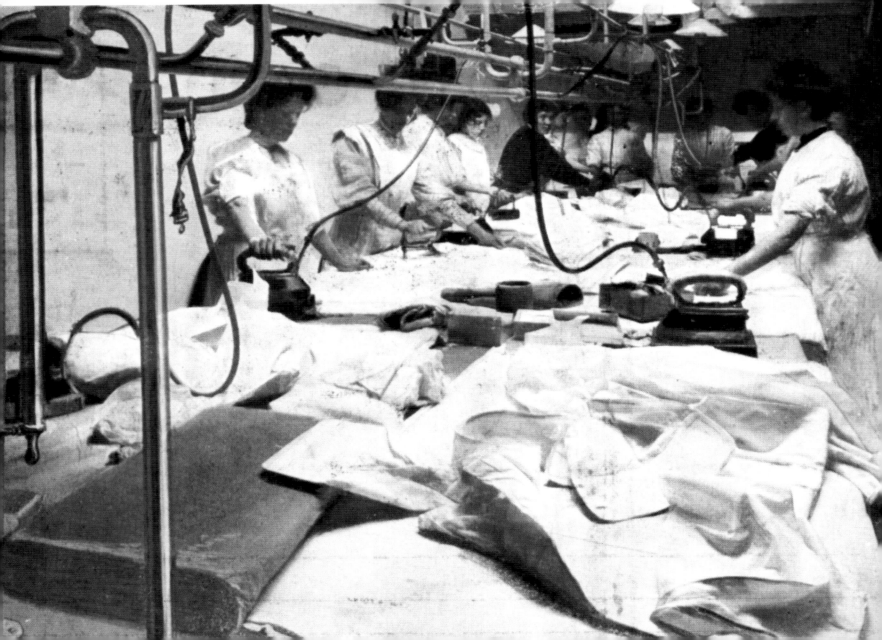

Ulster linen goods were displayed at the linen warehouse of Robertson, Ledlie, Ferguson & Co. who commissioned a new building, now occupied by Primark, on the junction opposite Castle Place in Belfast. The frontage of this tall, steel-framed structure opened in 1900 when horse-drawn buses were still used. The new premises were also known as the Bank Buildings and were described as being situated on the 'Charing Cross of Belfast – directly opposite the tramways junction where 1,100 cars pass and repass daily', with 'price lists with samples of every description of Belfast linens, orders sent carriage to any part of Great Britain'. Mail order had by then also become a common means of selling Ulster linen.

Previous page: Women in the Walpoles' Belfast factory, ironing what appear to be linen shirts or blouses. Advertising from 1895 to the 1930s indicates that Walpoles' made complete linen outfits, which were sold from London shops in New Bond Street and Kensington High Street, as well as handkerchiefs and household items. Linen damask and cambric handkerchiefs were produced in this building until the 1960s. Since then the former warehouse building has been converted for office use.

An unidentified group photographed in front of a trade stand exhibiting Irish lace and linen. Linen companies worked hard to market their work at trade fairs in Britain and abroad.

C. McKEOWN & CO.

(The Ulster Linen Depot),

46 MAIN STREET, PORTRUSH,

Irish Hand Embroidery. Specialists in Bedspreads, Tea, Tray,
Sideboard Cloths, Duchesse Sets, Handkerchiefs, Linen and
Damask Remnants, Stamped Goods for Embroidering.

THANK you for your kind patronage, and solicit your recommendation
of our goods to your friends. We can assure you that any orders
entrusted to us shall have our personal attention, so that customers
can rely upon being properly catered for. By the many unsolicited testimonials
and repeat orders which we receive from our customers, we have found by
experience that "a satisfied customer is our best advertisement."

C. McKEOWN, Proprietor.

T. B. & C.

Above: An advertising card used to promote the Irish Linen Depot when it opened in Portrush selling linen hand-embroidered tablecloths, bedspreads, napkins and tray cloths. In the early twentieth century linen embroidered blouses and collars were fashionable for women but the market for smaller household linen items endured, often bought as gifts, long after the decline in the fashion for linen clothes.

Right: The front of the Ulster Linen Depot in Portrush, photographed to celebrate the opening of a new premises at 46 Main Street around 1912. The shop was in competition with a number of other purveyors of Irish linen goods on Main Street, including Mrs Duff's, Pepper and Co. and the Swiss House. A local street directory suggests that McKeown's continued in business as a drapery shop until the late 1970s.

An idyllic view of two countrywomen as they embroider Irish linen, staged with a characterful old cottage in the background. The image was used to publicise Mrs Duff's Irish Embroidery Depot in Portrush which would have co-existed with McKeown's Irish Linen Depot nearby on Main Street. Linen tablecloths, napkins and handkerchiefs were embroidered with traditional images of flowers and shamrocks. The close weave of the linen fabric also lent itself to the technique of cutting out holes in the fabric which were then edged with decorative stitching work. Such items were sold to an increasing number of visitors to Portrush at the turn of the twentieth century when the north coast seaside town was a growing tourist resort, though this was a small part of the market. Over half the Irish linen produced was sold in the United States of America, followed by countries of the British Empire and South America.

Machinists employed in Robert Gilmore's factory on Rydalmere Street off Donegall Road, Belfast. Although working conditions for machine sewing were not humid and hot as in spinning and weaving factories, workers were still operating in cramped conditions and uncomfortably seated for long hours. In Belfast a hemstitching machine was invented in 1879 which increased production speed for linen items. Linen handkerchiefs were an important niche, a market which today has all but disappeared.

Barbour's works at Hilden Mills was by 1914 the largest linen thread producers in the world and employed over 2,000 people from the Lisburn area. The 34-acre site leased by William Barbour in 1824 was originally a bleach green operated by the de la Cherois family. The Hilden works had its own railway station on the Great Northern Railway line and, as the photograph indicates, coal was brought by barge from Belfast via the Lagan canal. A certain amount of flax was grown at Hilden to supply the works but such was the output that Barbour's also relied upon flax imported from the continent. From the 1950s a declining need for linen thread led to diversification into thread made from artificial fibres, although in 1978, when it was taken over by Hanson, it still exported to over 135 countries. Today the mill buildings are disused though a property company did buy them in 2017.

Wm. Barbour & Sons Linen Thread Works, Dunmurry.

The photograph shows a principal mill building at the Barbour's thread works. It is thought that thread making was introduced to Ulster in the late eighteenth century by John Barbour who settled, having come from Scotland, at Plantation near Hilden. Typically, as seen here, a mill building had four storeys. The first floor was used for the preparation of flax fibres by roughing and hackling processes whereby strands were refined and teased out into lengths that could be spun into yarn. The next two floors contained spinning rooms, while at the top were the reeling and winding areas for which lighter equipment was required. Once reeling was completed the thread was sent down by chute to the drying room which usually stood apart from the main building. The Barbour firm had branches in the USA and Europe. Machinery used at Hilden was imported from the United States and was still in use in 1967.

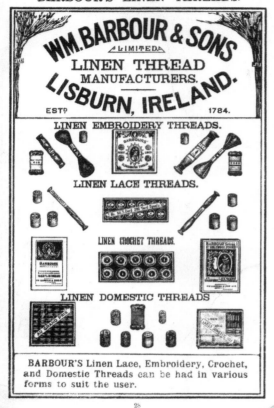

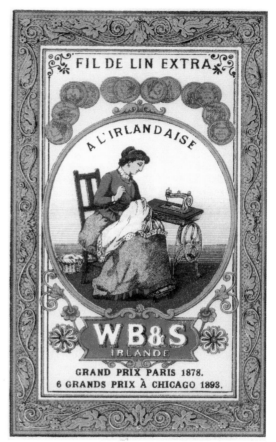

Left: A large range of domestic thread used for crochet, lace making, stitching seams and embroidery was produced by the Barbour company. Besides Hilden, the firm had further works near Lisburn at Sprucefield and Dunmurry, and also in the United States at Paterson, New Jersey, with a store and office in New York City. Descriptions of the time said that thousands of miles of thread were spun per day and it was claimed, 'If every man, woman and child in America used a spool of Barbour's sewing thread in a year the Paterson's mills could supply them.'

Right: Barbour's won awards for their thread in Paris in 1878 and Chicago in 1893 but those celebrated on this postcard represent a fraction of the prizes that included over twenty medals won at international trade exhibitions staged around the world after the Great Exhibition at Crystal Palace in 1851. Effective advertising was key to the success of this company and the Irish flax industry in general as a niche product for which most of the demand was from overseas.

The installation of netting equipment in 1905 at Barbour's mills allowed the development of a specialism in producing nets with linen fibre which was noted for its strength, lack of stretch and resistance to rot in water.

Nets produced for sea fishing by Barbour's sold well in the United States and Canada and were used for salmon fishing on the Western seaboards. The interests in netting were overseen by Sir Milne Barbour after he joined the business in 1888. He often travelled to Vancouver on sales visits. Though linen thread was durable, synthetic fibres were developed in later years after the Second World War.

The back view of Herdman's Mill at Sion Mills in Co. Tyrone with the fast-flowing waters of the River Mourne in the foreground. A record from 1640 shows that the site was originally a corn mill. The main mill building was designed by William Lynn of Lanyon Lynn Lanyon architects and built in 1853–55. An extension was added in 1888 and called the New End but the scaffolding on the left indicates this photograph was taken around 1907 when three new storeys were added. The design of the main mill was wider than usual for spinning mills of the time which enabled the Herdman enterprise to survive in later years by providing enough space to add larger machines that complied with new safety standards. Despite gradual improvements in working conditions and the endeavours of firms such as Herdman's to look after the welfare of employees, conditions in spinning mills were hard due to the steamy wet atmosphere where streams of hot water were used to keep the threads moistened, necessitating the women who tended the machinery to wear large oil-cloth aprons and to stand on the wet floors in bare feet.